Meg's Eggs
and
Other Stories

Illustrated by Nina O'Connell

CONTENTS

STECK-VAUGHN
C O M P A N Y

Meg's Eggs

"I have one egg.

Look at my egg,"

said Meg.

"I have two eggs.
Look at my eggs,"
said Meg.

"I have three eggs.
Look at my eggs,"
said Meg.

Come and see my eggs.

Come and look!

The Log

One chick got on the log.

Two chicks got on the log.

Three chicks got on the log.

Tom got on the log.

"No! No! No!"

said the chicks.

The Big Seed

"Here is a seed," said Meg.

"It is very big.

I will plant it."

So she did.

"I will give it some water,"
said Meg.
So she did.

"Look at it now," said Meg.

"I will give it some
more water."

So she did.

The plant grew and grew.

It grew taller than the chicks.

It grew taller than Meg.

"The plant looks like the sun,"
said Meg.
"It is a sunflower."

15

"We can eat all the seeds,"
said Meg.
And they did.